LEGENDS OF
KING DAVID

Retold for Jewish Youth

by S. SKULSKY
English by I. M. LASK
Illustrations by A. LUIZADA

SHULSINGER BROTHERS, PUBLISHERS
NEW YORK

translated from the Hebrew
"AGGADOT HAMELECH DAVID"
first published 1956

Printed in Israel by "Hamerkaz" Press, Tel-Aviv

CONTENTS

SOURCES

The legends adapted in this volume are taken from various collections of Midrashim. The final one is a reworking of the narrative poem "David's Tomb" by A. K. Shapiro.

1

DAVID AND HIS SHEEP

YOUNG DAVID was a handsome, brave and clever
boy. When his father Jesse saw how sensible
and reliable he was, he put young David in
charge of his flock. As the shepherd of his
father's flock, David always kept his mind set on
taking good care of them.

Every day at dawn he rose, and prayed to
the Lord. Then he took his food, his wallet and
his shepherd's crook, the end of which had been
shaped into a shepherd's pipe (a kind of flute).
He opened the sheep pen and led his flock out
to pasture.

Now the broad green meadows of Bethlehem run up and down the sides of the beautiful hills of Judea. The pastures are moist in the
mornings, with dewdrops gleaming and glisten-
ing like hundreds of thousands of coruscating
jewels laughing in the rays of the rising sun.

Here and there amid the fields of tall corn could be seen spacious pastures, the beds of dry watercourses on whose banks grew large green stretches of all kinds of grasses and weeds. But David would not let his sheep graze there. He did not want them to feed near the fields of strangers, for he knew that they might easily climb up into the fields and start eating the grain that was growing there. So he preferred to go far away, to places where there were no grain fields at all, but only vast acres of grass that did not belong to anybody.

Now it was not surprising that David played his shepherd's flute so well. In his soul God had planted the song of birds and the whisper of the wind that passes amid the treetops and branches, the rustling of ears of grain and the murmur of the running fountains.

His flock ambled ahead of him, and he kept his eyes on them. He watched every sheep and every little ewe, to make sure that none of them hung back. He helped the weak ones; and the tired ones he picked up one at a time and carried them over his shoulders. When they reached the meadow he watched to make sure that the weak little ones had their fair share of pasture; and

often he used to pluck soft, tender grass and feed them himself.

One day David came to very poor pasture-land, where there was only sparse and coarse grass. He feared that the stronger sheep would eat every blade of good grass, and leave nothing at all for the weaker ones. So he thought it over and decided what to do. First he sent the little kids and lambs into the field, and did not let the others enter until they had eaten to their hearts' content. When he saw that the younglings had eaten their fill, he sent the old sheep and goats so that they should eat the middling grass. Then, after they were also satisfied, he allowed the strong young sheep to enter the field and use their powerful teeth in chewing the hard stalks and blades of grass that were still left. That was how he made sure that all his flock ate their fair fill and were satisfied.

God saw how David provided for his flock and He approved very much indeed. And then it was that the Lord resolved to take David from his father's sheep-pens and anoint him as King of Israel. For the Children of Israel are the Lord's flock. They too need a trustworthy shepherd.

2

THE PITCHERS OF HONEY

When Saul was king of Israel there was a very rich man in Bethlehem, Judea. He had a young and beautiful wife. So good-looking was she that there was nobody to compare with her in the Land of Israel.

She was a kind-hearted and upright person. Her house was open to all the hungry and to anyone in distress. Never did she send a poor man away empty-handed. A beggar would always depart satisfied and with a blessing on his lips. And she lived modestly before God, respected by her neighbors and by all who knew her.

But her happy days did not last very long. Suddenly her husband became ill and took to his bed, from which he never rose again.

Only a short while after the poor widow ceased to mourn for him, the local governor offered to marry her. First he sent honorable people to her, to persuade her to agree. But when he saw that she was refusing steadily, he became angered, and began to find ways of causing her trouble. He imposed heavy taxes on the property she had inherited from her husband, for he hoped that in that way he would make her accept him. But the worse he treated her, the more she refused to marry such a hardhearted and tyrannous person. Finally he grew impatient and decided to force her to become his wife.

But the woman learned of this in advance; swiftly she hid all her money. She took all her gold coins and put them in earthenware vessels. Then she poured honey over the gold pieces, and in the presence of faithful witnesses she entrusted them to a good acquaintance of her dead husband; and she said:

"I fear evil from this nobleman and I must leave my home. Do me a great favor and look after these jars of honey for me until I can safely come back to Bethlehem."

This man had not forgotten all the kindnesses and favors which her dead husband had done for him, and he promised to guard her jars well. That very night the woman ran away to a distant village, where she disguised herself as a poverty-stricken and unhappy widow. Nobody knew her there at all.

When the governor learned that she had run away he became very furious and sent messengers and spies all over the country to look for her. They searched through the villages, they asked questions in the towns, they looked everywhere; but it was all in vain. The woman seemed to have vanished like a stone in the deep sea.

Years passed and people began to forget this woman who had fled. Only here and there did some of the poor folk still remember her. Meanwhile the jars of honey lay in the wine cellar of the man to whom she had entrusted them; for he had not forgotten his promise.

But one day his firstborn son was betrothed, and he made a feast for all the townsfolk. It was the custom in those days to honor guests with honey on such occasions, as a sign of the sweetness in which they hoped the young pair would live; and he acted according to the custom. So many guests came to the feast, though, that he did not have enough for all. What to do? Then he remembered the jars of honey which he kept in his cellar, and he said to himself: "If I use

some of the honey she left me I shall satisfy my guests; and tomorrow I can put it back."

So he went down to his wine cellar and took up a jar. To his astonishment he saw that instead of being full of honey it contained much gold, with just a little honey over it. He took another jar and found the same thing. He became very excited, for he thought to himself: "Now I have found both honey for my guests and money for myself."

So he took as much honey as he needed, and hurried back to his guests. He was so excited that he seemed to be drunk; he paid no attention to all the good wishes which everyone showered upon him.

The feast came to an end at last; the guests departed. Most of the night was already over, but he did not lie down to sleep. Instead he hurried back to the jars, and began to empty out the gold pieces by the light of a little oil lamp. He put the money in his own vessels and hid them in the ground. It was very dark outside, and in this darkness that came before dawn, nobody saw what he was doing. He finished as the first light began to show in the east, and went to bed.

Soon after dawn he rose again, mounted his

donkey, and went off to a distant village. There he bought a small quantity of old honey—as old as the honey he had taken from the jars—and he returned home. He filled a number of jars in the cellar, and then went on to another village, where he bought some more. This he did for several days, until he had filled all the jars which the woman had entrusted to him. And then he rested without worry, for he told himself: "If the woman should come today to ask for her jars I can return them, for I have bought honey that is as old as the honey which she left with me."

That day passed, and so did the months which followed. The woman did not come for her jars. But the man took care not to behave like a wealthy man, so that nobody should wonder how he had suddenly become so rich.

A few years later the governor was slain in one of the wars which the Children of Israel were waging against the Philistines. When the news reached the widow she removed the poverty-stricken garments and returned to Bethlehem, for now she had nothing more to fear. And she went to the man with whom she had left her jars of honey, and said:

"Now I have returned home. Please give

me back the jars I left in your hands; and may
the Lord repay you for the kindness you have
shown me in looking after them so faithfully."

"I have them all in good condition," said the
man. "Go and summon the witnesses in whose
presence you left the jars with me, and then take
what is yours."

So the woman fetched the witnesses and
received the jars of honey back. Not a single one
of them was missing. She had the jars brought
to her home. She opened them, but to her astonishment and despair she saw that they contained nothing but honey. She cried out in her grief
and hurt surprise, and hurried back to the man
who had kept the jars. And she said to him:

"Give me back my gold, for you have stolen
it all!"

The rogue answered calmly:

"Are you crazy, woman? You left me honey
and you demand gold? Whatever you entrusted
to me in the presence of witnesses, I have returned to you in their presence. Why do you ac-
cuse me of stealing? Aren't you satisfied with me,
that I looked after your jars so long without ask-
ing any money?"

Then the woman saw that he was a cunning

rogue, and that there was no way for her to get her money back. In her bitter despair she went to the town judge and asked him to try her case. The judge heard all she had to say and asked whether there were any witnesses, or some other way by which she could prove that there had been gold coins in the jars, and that the man had taken them. When she told him that she had no proof at all, he said:

"What can I do for you, my child, if you have no witnesses? Even if I could solve mysteries I would be unable to help you; you have no proof at all."

The woman burst into bitter tears and wept, for now she would remain penniless. Seeing this, the judge recognized that she was speaking the truth. Then he advised her to appeal to King Saul, in the hope that he would find some proof.

So the woman went to King Saul and told him what had happened. Now Saul was a kind and merciful king, who took up the cases of orphans and fought for the rights of widows. He listened to the words of the wronged woman. When he heard that she had no witnesses or other reliable proof that the man had stolen her money, he ordered heralds to go through the whole country and proclaim that anybody who had heard something, or could give the slightest reason for suspecting the man who had kept the jars, should come and inform him. Yet there was not a single person in the country who could bring any evidence, for the man had been very cautious and had lived modestly, behaving like an upright and honest person all the time. Not even among the guests at the feast, or the people who had sold him the old honey, was there a single man who suspected him.

And yet the woman was not prepared to accept the situation. She was a God-fearing person, and believed that the Lord would prove that she was telling the truth and would punish the man who had wronged her. So she came to the king a second time, yet weeping and wailing, and she cried:

"Is there no justice in Israel, to help a widow against the man who has done her wrong? Is it possible that now, when we have a king, a man can do whatever he pleases just as in the days of the Judges?"

The king felt very sorry for the poor woman, and he sent her to the Great Sanhedrin. That was the place where the seventy-one sages and

elders always sat studying the laws and commandments of the Torah, to decide how the laws
of Israel were to be enacted and carried out. It
was true that they did not deal with such money
claims but with criminal matters. Still, they heard
the woman's plea.

Yet even the Great Sanhedrin could not help
her, for how could they rely only on her claim
when she had no witnesses at all? So they questioned and cross-examined the man who had
kept her jars; but he simply kept repeating that
she was bringing a false charge against him. At
length they informed the king that they were
not in a position to pass judgment.

But by now this mysterious case had become
known in all the towns and villages in the country; it was a subject of general discussion, especially in Bethlehem, where it had happened.
People stood about at the gates of the city and
in the market-places, arguing back and forth.
Some said the woman must be right because they
remembered how honest she was, while others
insisted that the man who had kept the honey
jars could not have done anything wrong, because they knew *him* for a very honest man.

The grownups were not the only ones who

discussed the case. The youngsters also argued about it, while it became a game for the little children, and they played "The Widow's Trial." The only one who knew nothing at all about the matter was young David. For he was looking after his father's sheep; very early in the morning he went away to the hills with his flock; at sunset he came home tired and went straight to bed.

The poor despairing widow kept to herself after all this, and did not want to see her neighbors or those who knew her, for she could not find anybody who could comfort her or believe that she was telling the truth. For days on end she wandered along the mountain paths, softly weeping to herself over her bitter fate.

One day, as she was wandering so unhappily, she heard some beautiful music from a shepherd's pipe. For a moment she forgot what had happened to her, and stood still listening. Searching to find out where such lovely music came from, she saw a reddish-haired youngster leading his flock, with a little lamb over his shoulders as he played on his pipe. And now when she heard his tune her heart quivered and she burst out weeping yet once again.

When David saw this woman standing nearby, covering her eyes with her hands and weeping, he came over and asked:

"Why are you shedding tears, woman? Tell me what is oppressing your heart, for maybe I can help you."

At first the widow doubted whether it could really be worth her while to tell such a youngster about the wrong that had been done to her. What could such a boy do when wise old men had not been able to help? But then she thought of the wonderful music and melodies of this barefoot shepherd, and she saw how understanding and gentle was his gaze. So she told him briefly what her husband's old friend had done to her. She ended her tale and stood wringing her hands. For a moment David stood thinking, his bright far-seeing eyes staring ahead. He felt sure that she was telling the truth. Then he raised his eyes to her and said:

"Do not grieve so much, good woman. I am prepared to prove that you are right. But first you must receive permission from the king, so that such a young lad as I may plead your case. Then come to Jesse of Bethlehem, for I am his youngest son."

So the woman went to King Saul and said

to him, "My Lord the King, I have found a young lad who can show that my plea is indeed just."

The king sent for David at once; the young shepherd appeared before him and said:

"My Lord the King, you have called me, and I have come."

"Did you indeed tell this woman that you could prove that she is right?"

"It is true, my Lord the King."

"Then tell me, in the presence of the judges assembled here, how you wish to prove that there really were gold coins in those jars of honey."

Then David turned to the woman and said: "Fetch the jars which you entrusted to that man, and bring empty vessels also."

And to the king he said, "I pray you, my Lord King, call the witnesses before whom the widow gave her jars to the man, and summon also the man who held them."

Within a little while David's requests were carried out.

"Are these the jars which the woman deposited?" David asked the witnesses.

"Indeed they are," said they. "We recognize them by the marks that we ourselves made on them at the time."

Without another word, David took the jars that were full of honey, and emptied them one after the other into the empty vessels. Then he began to smash them in the presence of all the people assembled there. And lo and behold! Among the fragments of the broken jars there were several pieces to which gold coins still clung.

"Here is my witness!" cried David. And the face of the thief turned white as chalk.

There and then the king cried out to him: "Go and return the pledge to the woman; now we know your crime, and you will receive your punishment."

The judges wondered at David's wisdom and asked him how this idea had occurred to him. David explained that a thief will always do his stealing hastily, and all the more so this man; for the man could not know the number of gold pieces that had been put in the jars. Therefore he would not have been able to remove them all.

And so all Israel came to know that the spirit of God rested upon this lad, and that he was marked out for a great future.

3

DAVID IS ANOINTED KING

Now THE BIBLE tells us that when Samuel the prophet knew that King Saul no longer had the merit to make his children after him kings over Israel, he mourned very much. But the Lord said to him:

"How long are you going to mourn for Saul after I have found him unfitting? Fill your horn with oil and set out. I shall send you to Jesse of Bethlehem to offer up a sacrifice to the Lord. who is fit to be king."

Samuel promptly did what the Lord commanded. Fearing that Saul might learn that he was going to anoint another king in his place, he took a heifer and said that he was going to Bethlehem to offer up a sacrifice to the Lord. Then he filled his horn with the holy anointing oil which Moses had prepared in the wilderness, and which was used to mark new kings of Judah.

When Samuel arrived at Bethlehem the surprised elders of the city came to greet him. Samuel greeted them in return and reassured them, saying that he had merely come to sacrifice before the Lord God of Israel. Then he sent for Jesse and his sons.

Now Jesse had seven sons. Their names were Eliav, Abinadav, Shamma, Nathaniel, Raddai, Otzem and David. But only six of them came to the sacrifice, for the youngest was tending his father's sheep at the time, and was not in the city.

Samuel did not know which one the Lord had chosen to be king over Israel. He called forward Eliav the firstborn, saw that he was handsome and tall, and thought to himself: "This one deserves to be king."

Taking the horn in his right hand he wished to pour a drop of oil on Eliav's forehead, but found to his astonishment that there was no oil in the horn. At this he realized that the young man's appearance was misleading him; so had he been misled when he anointed Saul as king years before. Then the prophet understood that Man sees the outer appearance but the Lord looks at the heart. The vanishing of the oil was a sign from the Lord that this was not the son of Jesse chosen to be king.

And so the prophet blessed Eliav and took his hand away from the lad's head; and in that self-same moment the horn filled with oil. He called Abinadav, who also seemed to him worthy of a crown. But when he wished to pour out the oil, it simply did not flow. As before, Samuel passed his hand over the boy's head in blessing, and removed his hand; and the oil re-appeared. The same happened with Shamma the third son, and with all the others. They were all handsome and well-built, and they all found favor in his eyes. In the ordinary way any of them would have been fit to reign, though he, but the oil in his horn would not flow for any one of them.

All the elders of the city and the ordinary folk stood about watching, as the sons of Jesse approached Samuel while he held a horn over their heads and then blessed them. They saw the perplexed face of the prophet as the heavy horn which he lifted suddenly seemed to grow lighter, without a single drop falling to the ground. And they felt that something holy and mysterious was happening.

When the oil failed to flow over the head of Otzem, the sixth son, the prophet felt very perplexed indeed. The Lord had told him that He had chosen one of the sons of Jesse of Bethlehem to be king. Yet not one of them was anointed. For a moment Samuel stood thinking, his face clouded and troubled. Suddenly he started, and his face grew bright; and he turned to Jesse and asked him:

"Are these all the sons you have?"

"Why, no: the smallest is away with the sheep," whispered Jesse in great surprise.

"Send for him and have him brought here," said the prophet, "for we shall not sit down to the sacrifice until he comes."

And within a little while David came dashing from the pasture, his face and feet all dusty from the way.

When Samuel looked at the ruddy boy, a doubt passed through him. Could this one be worthy of the kingdom? Maybe he was like Esau, who was called Edom—"red"—because he was ruddy, and maybe he would shed blood like him? But as the very thought passed through his head, he heard the voice of the Lord: "Even if he sheds blood he will do it at My desire, when

I command him to wage battle against the enemies of My people. And as for you, gaze in his eyes."

So Samuel looked at the boy's eyes. They were exceedingly beautiful, bright and many-colored. In them he could see kindness, and pity, and love. His brow was broad and showed ample understanding. The hair of his head gleamed like fine gold. Samuel could not stop admiring him. for the appearance of the boy enchanted him. Then once again he heard the voice of the Lord:

"Come, anoint him, for this is he!"

So the prophet raised the horn of oil once again and held it over the boy's head. A drop of oil fell and gleamed on his reddish hair; it seemed to flash like a great diamond set in a golden crown. The prophet passed the oil round his head with his finger as though marking out a diadem. Then he passed it over the boy's eye-lashes, for that was the proper way of anointment.

A great light seemed to flash from between the lashes, like the light of the rising morning star; and Samuel knew that the Lord had chosen this lad as king. Then he offered up the sacrifice and returned to Rama.

4
DAVID SLAYS GOLIATH

ONE DAY, young David was pasturing his flock in the hills. He sat on a little hillock in the shadow of the one tallish shrub that grew there, for there was nothing else in all the great pasture round about him to provide shade against the hot sun. He sat moodily, not knowing what he desired. He could not play his shepherd's flute as usual, nor could he sing; for he grieved over the fate of his people.

The Philistines had gathered their army of soldiers and gone forth to fight Israel. Saul, of course, had also gathered his men and set out to fight them back. All the brave warriors in Israel had gathered together and gone to the battlefield. Among them were his three oldest brothers. Yet what would they be able to do against the might of the enemy, who had so many weapons of iron—swords and spears, shields and body armor? For in those days not a single iron worker was to be found in Israel, and only a handful of warriors had iron weapons. Would they be able to defeat their powerful enemy with bows and arrows and stout sticks?

David remembered how only a few days earlier he had begged his father to permit him to join his brothers in the field. But his father had refused, saying, "No, my son, you are still a young boy. There is no shortage of warriors in Israel, and the king does not need those who are as young as you are. Go and pasture the flock, for the shepherd is also a brave warrior."

"What was there brave about being a shepherd?" David went on thinking moodily. "Here the sheep are grazing all round me, and I sit here doing nothing! Then suppose ... suppose I go and run off to the battlefield without telling father," the thought stole into his mind. "No, no!" said he to himself, shaking the thought off. "I cannot do such a thing. No true shepherd will ever abandon his flock."

His thoughts ran on in this way till he fell asleep, his shepherd's crook besides him and his food sack at his head. For the heat of the day made him very weary.

All of a sudden a terrifying roar was heard at the far end of the pasture.

All the sheep began bleating and baaing in alarm, and dashed off in every direction. The noise woke David up, and to his astonishment he saw his sheep scattered all over the field. Gazing around to find out what had made them run every which way, he saw a young lion leap at one of the lambs. The lion touched it with his paw, and the quivering little thing burst into a heart-rending wail.

David jumped up, and instead of running away in terror he dashed at the lion. The beast had already dug its claws into the helpless lamb when David came dashing at it with his staff, beating it over the head with all his force. The lion growled, roared terrifyingly with pain, let the lamb go and staggered. Then it reared at its assailant.

David did not flinch. With one hand he caught the lion by the chin, while with the other he went on smiting it over the head, over the mouth, and over the eyes. Every blow landed home, and the bones seemed to give way under it. The lion howled and twisted with pain. It writhed and turned, trying to seize David with

its claws. But David gave it no chance; relentlessly he continued beating it until the beast fell lifeless to the ground.

David's staff had a shepherd's flute at one end. This David now put to his mouth, and began to play a familiar tune on it. And his sheep gathered together and came crowding round him, bleating happily, as though they wished to thank him for saving them.

When David went back home that evening with his flock, he wanted to go to bed at once without seeing his father. He felt ashamed that he had fallen asleep, and he did not want to have to tell his father.

But his father was waiting for him at the entry to the courtyard. So David stood silent and still in front of him, with his clothes torn and with many scratches on his face and his arms. Of course Jesse wanted to know what had happened, and David had to give him a full account. Then he stood still, sad and ashamed, expecting his father to scold and rebuke him for not staying awake. And then, to his astonishment, his father bent over him and kissed him on the head.

David raised his eyes and stared at his father, and saw to his surprise that the old man's face was bright with joy. Then he heard the old man saying to him:

"Why, that is what I told you, my son. A shepherd is also a brave warrior. Yet you wished to leave the flock and go to the battlefield. After this you will always remember that it is not only in warfare that the hero shows his bravery. But indeed, I am proud of you, my son!"

As he said this he passed his gentle hand over the boy's reddish curls and added:

"Now I have good news for you, my son. Tomorrow you will go to your brethren at the field of battle. Take a measure of parched wheat with you, and ten loaves of bread for them. And take these ten pieces of cheese as well. They are a gift from me to the captain of the thousand. Visit your brothers and see that all is well with them, and then come back home."

David's joy was boundless as he listened to his father's instructions. At last he could go to the battlefield. And even though he was not going in order to fight but just to visit his brothers, still he would be able to see with his own eyes, the brave and courageous warriors of Israel.

So David rose with the dawn and went to the sheep pens as though he wished to say goodbye to his flock. There he found a shepherd waiting, whom his father had asked to take his place. David told him what special attention had to be given to the sheep, and which of them had to be looked after in particular. Then he turned and went his way.

The sun rose high, and its blazing rays began to have their effect on the boy with the fine eyes and reddish hair, who was walking so vigorously towards Socho in Judah, to the place where the soldiers of Israel had taken up their stand. The load that David was carrying on his shoulder was a heavy one, but he scarcely felt it in his joy at this welcome duty, which his father had given him. Although he had not eaten since he had risen early that morning, he felt neither hungry nor thirsty; and he did not wish to lose a moment.

The noon-hour was approaching when he began to see signs of the battlefield. The corn fields were abandoned and desolate. The tracks of men, the hoofmarks of horses, and the marks of wagon wheels grew more plentiful from moment to moment on all sides of him. From time to time a swift runner, or a military guard who had come out to patrol the neighborhood, would pass him by, making sure that none of the enemy lay hidden in ambush. The closer he came to the camp the more often did the guards stop him and ask him what he was doing there. He answered all their questions wisely and to the point.

At last he saw the camp in the distance. First it seemed to him that there must be a huge flock of sheep there, but he quickly began to identify each section by the banner of its tribe, while the noise and tumult of a vast multitude filled the air like the roar of an angry sea.

David speeded up his steps. Large drops of sweat ran down from his brow. The heavy load on his shoulder swung and heaved from side to side as he hastened on his way.

At the entrance to the camp, the guards stopped him. When he told them why he had come, he was led to the section of Judah. In the distance he recognized his three brothers at the entrance to their tent.

"Eliav! Abinadav! Shamma!" cried David joyfully. "Is everything well with you?"

His brothers hastened over to him, and took him into their tent; they asked after their father and all at home, while they began eating the food which he had brought with him. He also ate, his appetite surprising his brothers. Looking in their faces he in turn was surprised. He had hoped to see them bright and cheerful, but their faces were heavy with worry. He did not dare to ask what the matter was, but he did wish to give his father's gift to the captain of their thousand.

"Just you stay here in the tent," said Eliav to him, "and we will hand over the gift."

"Listen, brothers," David entreated them, "please let me go and see the camp. I did not come here to rest. When I go back to my flock tomorrow, I shall rest all day long."

Eliav looked at him long and searchingly, then shook his finger at him and said:

"I know you, David. Why did you come here? And with whom did you leave the handful of sheep in the wilderness? I know your naughtiness; I'll wager you only came here to see the fighting."

David wished to stand up for himself, for he could not understand why his brothers were in such a bad mood; but he decided that it would be wiser to keep silent and say nothing. So he remained at the camp a little while longer; but

when he saw that his brothers were always keep-
ing an eye on him, and they just would not let
him go at all far from the tent, he decided to
return home at once, as his father had ordered
him to do.

After that Jesse used to send his son regular-
ly to see how his older brothers were getting on.
Finally, one day, David succeeded in getting
away from the tent and reaching the center of
the camp; for the tribes were stationed in a kind
of very large half-circle. Standing there, he
could see the whole lie of the land. He saw the
Philistines stationed on the mountain on one side
and Israel on the mountain on the other side,
with the deep valley of Elah lying between.
Turning his gaze to the camp of Israel he saw
the countless tents and the soldiers moving to
and fro between them, all of them nervous, unhappy and sad. He began to be alarmed. Then
he raised his eyes and looked at the mountain
opposite. It was a bright scene that he saw. The
magnificent and bedecked Philistine tents shone
and gleamed in the distance. Soldiers armored
from head to foot were striding about there,
laughing and joking, singing and playing; they
leaped about and wrestled happily. Copper hel-

mets gleamed and flashed in the sunlight. Spears and lances sparkled and glittered. Everything over there spoke of victory, victory, victory!

"What has happened to the warriors of *my* people?" wondered David anxiously. "Is this the first time that they are facing these ornamented heathen soldiers? Why are they walking about so sadly? Have they lost heart?"

While he stood there wondering, he saw something that utterly amazed him. Out of the Philistine army strode a fighting man, a real giant, with a copper helmet on his head, and dressed in chain mail. On his legs he wore copper greaves, and a spear was slung between his shoulders. As for his lance, it was as thick and heavy as a wooden beam. Before him walked his aide-de-camp, carrying his long shield.

When this giant appeared, a deathly silence spread through the camp of Israel, and David heard a terrified whisper among the people standing beside him, "Goliath has come to curse and abuse the forces of Israel all over again."

All of a sudden the voice of Goliath resounded from the opposite hill:

"Choose yourselves a man and let him come down to me! If he can fight with me and over-

49

come me in battle, we shall be your slaves. But if I can overcome him, you will be our slaves and serve us.... Come, send me a man and let us fight together...."

So Goliath declared, and then he waited a moment. When he saw that nobody was leaving the camp of Israel to meet him, he began shouting his contempt and mockery; he cursed the army of Israel and the name of the God of Jacob.

"Give me a man and let us do battle together," he repeated; and the soldiers of Israel heard him and lowered their heads in shame, standing pale, angry and helpless. It was true that there were any number of brave warriors among them. They were quite prepared to risk their lives and stand face to face with the Philistines. No, it was not the danger which made them flinch from going to meet this giant of a Philistine—but what about the responsibility? It was all very well for a man to go and die a hero's death and save his own honor, as might easily happen. But in that case their people would be doomed to servitude. Any number among them were prepared to sacrifice themselves, yet was any one likely to overcome that giant, who was one mass of iron and copper? And if anybody were to volunteer, he would be someone foolishly chasing after fame, but he was almost certain to bring not victory but slavery for his entire people.

Goliath stood there for a while, shouting his abuse and derision. At last he burst out in jeering laughter, and returned to his camp. His laughter echoed through the air, piercing David's heart like a sword. Now he knew why the camp of Israel was so gloomy, why all the warriors were so sad.

"That Philistine has been mocking us for forty days already," he heard one of the men saying with gritted teeth. "He will appear again in three hours or less."

"And our King sits in his tent like a grief-stricken mourner," sadly added another.

David could no longer bear the shame of his people and the grief of his king. In a rush of emotion he said to himself: "I shall go and fight the Philistine, for I trust in the Lord!"

He joined the men standing nearby and asked, "Who is this heathen Philistine, who mocks the army of the living God?"

Then the soldiers started telling him how Goliath came and did the same thing twice a day. They told him something more: The king had proclaimed that if any man should smite the Philistine and lay him low, he would be made very rich, and would also marry the king's daughter.

"I shall beat him, for I have faith in the Lord!" cried David.

This brought a smile to their lips, and the word went round the camp.

And so King Saul was soon told that there was a young lad in the camp who said that he could beat the Philistine. This interested the king, and he sent for him. He was curious to see what stuff this lad was made of.

So David was brought before the king. The boy greeted him and said:

"Let your servant go and do battle with this Philistine."

Saul gazed thoughtfully at the lad standing in front of him. Then he said:

"You will not be able to prevail against him. For you are still a young fellow, and he has been trained since his youth to do battle as a warrior."

Then David told Saul and all the officers and counsellors standing around how he was a shepherd looking after his father's flocks. He told them how with his own hands he had slain a great bear that had come to steal a sheep from the flock. Only a few days earlier, he added, he had killed a young lion with his staff. Was the Philistine likely to be stronger than a lion? David ended his words: "The Lord who delivered me from the lion and the bear will also deliver me from this Philistine."

They listened to these assured words in amazement, for they saw how brave and daring the young fellow was. The king decided to give him his chance, and permitted him to go out against the Philistine. He added that David had better wear his—Saul's—armor; he gave him a copper helmet, and with his own hands tied his sword round his waist.

"Go in the name of the God of Israel," the king blessed him. David left the tent, but turned back at once and said, "I simply cannot walk in these, because they weigh too much. I shall just take my own weapons."

Saying this, he removed the royal armor, and went out to meet Goliath the Philistine face to face; and all the weapons he had with him were his staff and his sling.

As David started down the side of the

mountain on which stood the camp of Israel, the king, the officers and the soldiers all wished him God-speed. David felt that they were all concerned for him. So he put the shepherd's flute at the end of his staff to his mouth, and began piping a song that was a prayer to the Lord. When the men of Israel saw how calm the lad was and how greatly he trusted the Lord, they also became calm.

David swiftly reached the valley between the two hills. There he began to seek smooth pebbles for his sling, hunting here and there. Suddenly he heard a clattering and a rattling. and saw ever so many small sharp stones gathering at his feet by themselves. He stretched out his hand and five smooth sharp stones jumped into it. And David felt as though each of them were telling him:

"I, I am the one that must slay this wicked man, this accursed idol-worshipper."

He took the first stone that had come into his hand, set it in his sling and began to climb the slope on which the Philistine army stood. It was just the time when Goliath came out again to curse and revile the army of Israel, for he did this twice a day. Then suddenly he saw that somebody from the Israelite army was approaching. He stopped shouting and turned and moved towards David, while his armor-bearer went ahead of him, carrying his heavy shield.

The Philistine stared when he saw that it was a small lad who was coming up to meet him, without any weapons that he could see except a shepherd's staff and a sling. He stared and said contemptuously:

"Am I a dog for you to come up against me with sticks? Come over here and let me give your flesh to the birds of heaven and the beasts of the field."

And David answered with assurance:

"You are coming up against me with a sword and a lance and a spear, but I bring the name of the Lord of Hosts against you."

At this Goliath grew very angry and ran towards David. David in turn ran toward Goliath, and stopped only a few paces away from him. Just as the Philistine dashed at him with a spear, he aimed his sling. The stone hissed out and sank into the Philistine's temple.

The blow set Goliath reeling. He cried out and tottered, and then he fell his full length to the ground; his head just touched David's feet.

David placed one foot on the back of his neck and pressed him down to the ground, so that his mouth was full of earth. At the same time he tugged Goliath's sword out of its scabbard and cut off the giant's head. He picked the head up in both his hands and raised it aloft, so that the soldiers in the two camps should see what he had done.

The Children of Israel shouted aloud for victory, in great triumphant joy. When the Philistines saw in their amazement that their hero had fallen, they fled in panic for their very lives. But the warriors of Israel were already in pursuit of them. They caught up with the enemy and smote them very heavily indeed. So was Israel victorious because of David, who trusted in the Lord.

5

DAVID WISHES TO UNDERSTAND

When David tended his father's sheep, he used to enjoy sitting in the pasture on a little hillock or in the shadow of a tall tree, playing on his flute or thinking about the world and its Maker. He always wished to know the meaning of everything that he saw, and the purpose of each object and creature that he came across. He tried to reach the ultimate meaning of its creation, and when he discovered such a secret, his heart would fill with joy. Then he would sing the praises of the Lord, who had created His universe with so much wisdom and understanding.

Indeed, there was really nobody in the whole wide world who could sing as well as he did. For his songs were full of feeling and knowledge, since he had pondered and thought about the works of the Lord until he understood how truly great and wonderful indeed they are.

One day David sat beside an abandoned hut. His sheep were grazing all round him and he was staring about, looking for something that could interest him. His eyes fell on a corner of the hut where a spider was spinning her web. Round and about scuttled the spider, this way and that, and tiny thin fine threads spun out and were turned into an embroidered network.

David wondered at the work of this creature and he asked himself a very big question. Why was this spider toiling so much? Did anybody get any benefit from its webs? Would anybody come and use them in making a cover for his body? He thought and thought but could see no purpose in this. Into his heart there crept a bit of doubt that after all the Lord had created creatures which served no useful end.

While he was still thinking in this way a wasp came, buzzed and flew at the spider and ate it up. David wondered even more, and he asked himself further, "Now look at this wasp. She does not make any honey, and she actually destroys other creatures. Why was she created?"

And so this time David did not sing songs of praise to the Lord, but began to doubt all His works instead.

However, the Lord saw his thoughts and said: "The day will come when David himself will recognize the use and purpose of these creatures."

In due course David grew up. His fame spread far and wide in the Land of Israel, because he smote Goliath the Philistine and afterwards proved to be a great warrior. But then the Lord aroused the wrath of King Saul against him and would not let him be. So David fled and hid himself in the mountains. One day he ran to hide in a cave, and he sat there with thudding heart, for he knew that the king's men were close behind and might easily follow his footsteps. Yet God who had saved him until then came and helped him once again. He sent a swarm of spiders, and during the night they spun a huge thick web over the entrance to the cave. When Saul approached and saw how thickly covered the entrance was with webs, he did not even bother to look inside. For, said he, if David had entered he would have torn the webs.

Looking out of the cave, David saw that Saul was turning away. Then he remembered how he had doubted God about the spider when he was young. And when he left the cave he took a spider in his hand and said, "Blessed may you be before the Lord, for now I have learned that His deeds are great indeed, and that there is a purpose for all His creatures."

A few days later David found Saul sleeping in his tent at noon, while Abner slept at the entrance to the tent. Now David could easily slay both. He wanted that when Saul awoke, this king should know that David could have harmed him, but did not choose to. He decided to take away the flask of water at the king's head. He went to the entrance, stood between Abner's feet, picked up the flask and prepared to go; but at that moment Abner turned over in his sleep and closed his legs on David. So David stood there as though he were imprisoned, pinned by Abner's legs and unable to move. Seeing how dangerous his plight was he raised his eyes to the Lord. And the Lord sent a wasp which stung Abner in the leg so that he turned over back again, and David escaped. Then he remembered how he had also doubted God about the wasp in his youth; he saw that God forgets nothing, and that all His deeds have their purpose. And so, once more he began singing songs of praise and thanksgiving.

6

DAVID CAPTURED BY YISHBI

Now DAVID was a warrior whose like you would
not find in the whole world. One of his arrows
was enough to kill eight hundred men together,
so swift and piercing it was. But he began to feel
proud of his prowess, and he went about boasting, "There never has been a hero like me, nor
is there any other now, and there never will be
either."

Now the Lord was very displeased with
him, and decided to teach him a lesson. Said He:

"David, David, how long will you keep on
boasting of your bravery and forgetting the
wickedness of your wars? Because of you all the
people of Nob the city of the priests were killed;
Saul and his three sons were slain. Would you
sooner have Me make an end of your children,
or would you rather fall into the hands of an
enemy?"

And David answered, "I would far sooner fall into the hands of the enemy and not lose my children."

One day David went to the village called Sechar Bazzai to hunt. With him went Avishai ben Tzeruya, the brother of his general Joab. Suddenly a lithe, handsome deer appeared before them. They began pursuing it, but it was exceedingly swift, and it leapt and sprang and bounded, and soon it had escaped. But David made up his mind that he must catch it, for no creature that he hunted had ever escaped from him. He could not know that the Lord had sent this deer especially to entrap him. So David ran one way and Avishai another, to catch the deer between them. But on the way the lace of Avishai's shoe became undone, and while he was standing tying it up David vanished, and Avishai did not know where to look for him.

Meanwhile, David did not even notice that while chasing the deer he had entered Philistine territory. He kept after it until, suddenly, he raised his eyes and saw a handsome castle before him. He entered, and then heard a man roaring:

"O you murderer, you who killed my broth-

er Goliath! Now that you are here, I shall take full vengeance on you."

This was Yishbi, Goliath's brother. He was a giant, very tall and strong, just as his brother had been. He simply took hold of David and thrust him into a little space in the wall. He tied his hands and feet, threw him to the ground, and put a board over him—the kind that was set on top of olives and covered with weights to press them. Then Yishbi sat down on this board, saying, "Now I'll squash David to death." Sitting like that he ate and drank and laughed in great merriment. Yet how astonished he was when he stood up and found that the place where David was lying had sunk down in the ground, so that David lay there unharmed.

At this Yishbi became absolutely furious. He took hold of David and flung him up in the air; before ever David came down, the giant had placed his spear so that his captive must fall on the point. But David prayed to the Lord, who kept David hanging in the air between heaven and the earth. Yishbi danced with impatience, his spear in his hand and his lips foaming. He jumped higher and higher, yet he could not reach

David, who kept floating in the air and simply did not fall to the earth.

Meanwhile Avishai was seeking David and did not know where to look for him. He saw a pool of water and wanted to quench his thirst. Suddenly the water turned to blood before his eyes, and Avishai bcame greatly alarmed. For he realized it was a sign that his king was in great danger. He stood up and began to run, and found a dove moaning and plucking at her feathers. He grew even more alarmed, for he understood that the dove was telling him to help David quickly, since he was in great distress.

While he ran this way and that he saw a handsome tower in front of him. He entered; and there he saw Orpa, the mother of Yishbi, sitting spinning thread at a spindle. He asked her if David was there, but she did not wish to say anything. Then he understood that David must be in this building. Suddenly Orpa let the spindle drop, and Avishai understood that she wanted to signal to someone that he had come. So he caught hold of the spindle and dashed her brains out with it. Then he went to the court-yard behind the tower, where he saw David fluttering in the air while Yishbi leaped about in great anger as he tried to reach him with his spear, but could not.

Avishai stood at a distance and shouted to David:

"Tell me, my lord King, why you are in this great distress?"

So David told him in a few words how he had boasted of his bravery, and how the Lord had handed him over to his enemy because of it. When Avishai heard these words he implored the king to pray to the Lord and beg for forgiveness and atonement for his sin. When the Lord would see that he had repented, and was really humbled in his spirit, He would forgive him and deliver him.

David accepted his good counsel and did pray. No sooner did he end his prayer than he slowly began to glide to earth. When Yishbi saw David falling he swiftly thrust his spear at him, but David leaped backwards, about twenty paces in a single bound.

At this sight Yishbi grew terrified. For, thought he, if this fellow can jump twenty yards back, he certainly can jump forward very well. He no longer had the courage to pursue David. But David still feared the giant Philistine. When he saw him standing at a loss and doing nothing, he waved to Avishai and both of them began to run. At the sight of their panicky flight Yishbi came to his senses and began to chase them.

In this way he ran after them to a spot that was called Bi-Trei. Here they stopped running, and Avishai began to taunt the huge Philistine, shouting: "Cannot two young lions overcome one old one? You had better go home and dig a grave for your mother Orpa."

When Yishbi heard that his mother was dead, he felt faint and weak.

Seeing that David and Avishai had now approached him he began to entreat them not to kill him. But David knew that if they allowed him to remain alive, he would return to the Philistines and would boast that ten men had set out to kill him and he had overcome them; he would spread shame over the good name of the warriors of Israel. So they both fought him and killed him.

In due course David slew the third son of Orpa as well. This was the one who had six fingers on each hand and six toes on each foot; he was the brother of both Goliath and Yishbi.

Then the inhabitants of Jerusalem and all

the Children of Israel knew that the Lord had indeed decreed the destruction of the family of Orpa. For this was Orpa the Moabite woman who had been the sister-in-law of Ruth, the great-grandmother of David.

When they talked about this, the people of Israel would say, "The sons of the kissed one fell at the hands of the sons of the faithful one." By this they meant that the sons of Orpa, who had kissed Naomi and then abandoned her, had been slain by the descendant of Ruth who had remained faithful to her mother-in-law Naomi, and had followed her, saying, "Wherever you will go I shall go, and wherever you will stay I shall stay; your people are my people, and your God is my God. Where you shall die I shall die, and there I shall be buried. So may the Lord do to me and so may he continue, for only death will divide me from you."[1] For that was why she had merited to become the ancestor of David, the mother of kings.

All his life long David remembered what Yishbi had wished to do to him, and he no longer boasted of his bravery.

---

1. Ruth 1:16 - 17.

7

THE LAST OF THE IDOLS

THREE YEARS after the death of Saul a great famine began in the country. The fields grew barren and desolate. The corn perished as it grew because there was no water. David knew that this had come from the Lord, for in the Torah is written: *If you serve other gods and bow down before them, the wrath of the Lord will be kindled against you. He will seal the heavens and there will be no more rain, and the earth will not give her yield.*[1] So he decided that he must find out whether any among the Children of Israel still worshipped idols.

The king's men went off to inspect all the cities and villages of the country. They sought everywhere, but could not find a single Israelite who was worshipping strange gods. David re-

---

1. Deuteronomy 11:16-17.

joiced when he heard from his messengers that idol worship had come to an end in the country, and he knew that this was not the reason why the Lord had sent famine upon the land.

Now in due course there appeared a man whose name was Jonathan ben Gershom. This man wandered from place to place looking for a good way to earn a living. When he came to the tribe of Dan he found them bowing down before a graven image. He suggested that they should appoint him as a priest to their idol, and they agreed. But they quickly learned that the behavior of this priest was very strange. For instance, a man and woman came to bow down to the image, bringing handsome gifts for the priest, but the priest would ask them:

"How old are you?"

"My wife is fifty and I am sixty," the man would make answer.

"Why, what a silly old pair you are!" cried the priest. "Don't you feel ashamed to bow down before an idol which is only two years old and not a day more?"

The man and his wife went off feeling ashamed of themselves, and in their hearts they swore that they would never sacrifice again to idols.

Then there was another occasion when a man who was blind in one eye brought a gift of fine meal for the idol. Said he to the priest, "I have come to bow down, and I have brought a gift with me as well. But I want you to pray to the idol to return the lost light of my eye to me."

"Why, what a fool you must be," laughed the priest. "Fancy a one-eyed person begging for sight from something that is blind in both eyes! Just look at this idol!"

And this man also went his way feeling ashamed of himself, and thinking that an idol made by flesh and blood could not really be of much help.

A few days later a woman came carrying a child who had been ailing in the legs from birth. She too bowed down to the ground in front of the idol, and began to pray and entreat for strength in her son's legs so that he should be able to walk like everyone else. But when Jonathan ben Gershom heard her, he scolded her, saying: "Dear, dear, what a foolish and silly woman! First ask this copper idol to shift from his place and show your son *how* to move a leg.

Maybe your boy will be able to learn how to walk from that!"

So this poor woman also went away feeling foolish and ashamed of herself.

The word spread in the Tribe of Dan that the priest despised the idol and mocked at everybody who came to bow down before it. Soon a headstrong man went to the priest and asked him: "Why do you drive people away from the idol which you are supposed to serve? Did we choose you as priest for that?"

Jonathan calmly answered: "I only hired myself out as a priest for the sake of a living. If your tribe were to come and tell me to put out the eyes of the idol and they would give me my pay, I would do what they desired with a glad heart." And in order to prove how powerless the idol was, he went over to it and spat on its head contemptuously.

When the man saw what the priest did, he also spat at the face of the graven image, for seeing this, he could no longer fear the little statue, or respect it.

Now David also heard about this strange priest. He summoned him and asked him: "Jonathan ben Gershom, do you not belong to the

Tribe of Levi? How can you serve as a priest to an idol?"

"I make my living that way," he answered, "and I act as a priest only in order to lead the Children of Israel away from their evil paths."

But David wished him to serve the Lord in truth and honesty, so he set him in charge of his treasures and said to him:

"From now on you will no longer be called Jonathan but Shevuel, for that means that you have returned to the living God."

And so there was no more idol-worship in the days of King David, for the idols had vanished from the country.

8

DAVID AT WAR

WHEN THE TIME CAME that David fought the
Philistines they remembered how he had killed
their champion Goliath, and they became greatly frightened. They sent him their elders, who
said to him:

"You are one of the descendants of Isaac;
there was a time when he cut off a piece of the
bridle of the donkey on which he rode, and gave
it to our forefathers as a sign that there should
be peace between him and ourselves forever. Do
you intend now to violate this covenant?"

David saw that the Philistines were only
looking for an excuse, with false claims and ar-
guments. For they had already broken this oath
and covenant many times in making war on Israel. In spite of this he did not wish it to be said
that he was following in the paths of the idol-
worshippers and behaving like them, as long as

they had something to depend on; for the sign of the covenant, the piece of the bridle, was in their possession after all.

And so he asked them to bring him the piece of the bridle. The Philistines handed over th sign of the oath to him. Thereupon David said to them: "Now you have returned me this sign of the covenant which was entrusted to your hands. The oath of my father Isaac is annulled from this day on, after all you have done to my people."

Then he went up against the enemy with his warriors. David's men seized the Philistines even as they were prepared for battle, and stretched the men out on the ground in a single row; then they measured them with the strip of the bridle; two measures to be put to death and one to be left alive.

After this David sent Joab ben Tzeruya, his brave general, to fight against Aram Naharyim and Aram Tzoba. The inhabitants of Aram, which is Syria, grew very much afraid, and they sent their elders to Joab and said to him: "If you are one of the sons of Jacob, we must remind you that he made a covenant with our father Laban; and they even set up a heap of stones as an everlasting witness, which you call Gal Ed and we call Yegar Sahadutha."

Joab had no answer for this, for he saw that their argument was a just one. So he let them be and proceeded to wage battle against Edom.

But the men of Edom sent *their* elders to him and said: "Have you forgotten what is written in the Torah?—*This is far enough for you, go round the mountain.*[1] And it meant: Turn away from Mount Se'ir where the sons of Esau dwell, for that is intended as the heritage of Edom."

Joab realized that their claim was also a just one, so he let them be. But he did not wish to return empty-handed, so he set out against Ammon and Moab. But the men of Moab had heard that Joab observed the Commandments of the Torah, since he had turned away from their neighbor Edom; they also sent their old statesmen to him, and they spoke: "How can you be thinking of fighting against us and conquering our country, when it is written in your very own Torah, *Do not distress Moab?*"[2]

So Joab saw that he could not fulfill the

---

1. Deuteronomy 2:3.   2. Deuteronomy 2:9.

orders of David his king. He sent him a letter in which he reported all that the nations had argued against him when he set out with his army to conquer them.

However, David well understood that these nations did not desire to observe the Torah, since they had broken everything it commanded, and more than once. He removed his royal garb and put on ordinary clothes. He took off his crown and put on a mantle like one of the simple folk, and so he came before the Sanhedrin and said:

"My masters, I have come to you just as an ordinary member of the people, simply in order to learn. Yet if you are prepared to give me permission, I shall teach. I sent Joab to Aram Naharyim and to Aram Tzoba and to Edom and Moab, and they all spoke of ancestral covenants and the words of the Torah. Yet surely they were the first to disregard what is written there! What did Edom answer Moses when he wished to pass that land? *Thou shalt not pass through me, lest I come forth against thee with the sword.*[3] And did not the men of Ammon help the soldiers of

---

3. Numbers 20:18.

Amalek when they waged war against Ehud ben Gera? And did not Rishatayim king of Aram, and Eglon king of Moab, enslave the Children of Israel in the day of the Judges?"

After the Sanhedrin had heard the words of David to the end, they said:

"You are correct. Go and fight against these people, and may the Lord prosper you."

David promptly sent the reply of the Sanhedrin to his general. Then Joab went first against Edom, and he defeated them badly. Yet even before he vanquished them completely he proceeded against Aram, saying, "If I first destroy Edom and Moab and then go against Aram, there will be no water available for us on the way back."

So he first defeated Aram and then went back and conquered Moab. After that he went and defeated Edom a second time, and made it pay a tribute.

9

A TRUE JUDGE AND
LOVER OF RIGHTEOUSNESS

DAVID WAS a true judge; he loved righteousness, and strove always to give just decisions. One day a poor man was brought before the king because he owed money to his rich neighbor. The poor man claimed that for a long time he had lived at peace with his neighbor; he had had a plot of land as big as his neighbor's, and neither of them had known want. In those days it happened quite often that his neighbor would come to borrow something, and he would always let him have it and would never think twice about it. But now he had lost all his property, while his neighbor was growing richer from day to day. When he was down to the last crust of bread and had no way of supporting his hungry household, he appealed to his rich neighbor and borrowed some money from him. But now the rich man did not wish to remember all the favors and kindnesses that he himself had done him in the past. Instead, he not only refused to help him in his distress, but he now began to demand that the poor man pay the debt, even though he knew that this impoverished neighbor had nothing with which to pay.

"And so I see," the poor man finished, "that my neighbor is a wicked man and it would be proper that I should demand my own back from him. As for the money I borrowed, it is really my own money, considering all the favors I did for him, and therefore I shall not return it."

The king questioned the witnesses, and he found that all the poor man had said was true. In spite of this he found him guilty, for he said, "You borrowed money, and it is your duty to pay your debt."

The poor man saw that the king had judged him truly and justly, and that he did not give preference to the poor, but held everybody equal who came for trial. He admitted his transgression and said: "To be sure, I am doing something wrong to my neighbor when I do not pay him; yet where shall I find the money to pay my debt when there is not even food for my family in my home?"

Then the king took money out of his own pocket and paid the debt. In this way he acted according to the letter and the spirit of the law.

It was not only toward others that he acted in truth and justice, but also toward himself. One day, while he was fighting the Philistines, he wished to offer a libation or drink offering to the Lord. Then he turned to his men and said to them: "How shall I offer a libation to the Lord when we have no water here?"

There and then three warriors volunteered and said to the king:

"Do not grieve, your Majesty, we shall go and bring you water."

"And where will you find water?" asked David the king.

"Why, we three shall go to the enemy camp and force our way to the fountain and draw water from it."

So the three warriors went off to the Philistine camp. When the Philistines saw them they mocked and laughed at them, saying, "What can these three do against our great and mighty camp? If they dare to come up against us we shall crush them level with the very dust."

While they were talking to one another the

three warriors went into action. The first cut his way through, slaying a hundred on his left and felling two hundred on his right. The other who followed him cleared the corpses out of the way and made a passage, so that the third warrior could go to the fountain. When the Philistines saw this they scattered in every direction, while the warriors drew their water and returned to David's camp.

Meanwhile the sun had grown hot and was blazing like a furnace. David was dreadfully thirsty. His lips almost cracked with thirst. When the three warriors saw how parched their king was, they entreated him to drink a little of the water they had brought from the enemy camp. But David answered: "Far be it from me to do such a thing before the Lord. For this water has been brought only in order to pour out a libation before God."

Meanwhile his servants had set up a *bamah,* a kind of crude altar; there he now poured out a libation before the Lord; and he did not take a single drop of that water to his lips.

10

DAVID ACCEPTS JUDGMENT

SOME THINGS in David's life were tragic, and brought him great suffering. But never was he so hurt and saddened as when his own son Absalom rebelled against him. Absalom gathered an army to fight David, for he wished to kill his father and reign in his place. David fled and climbed the Mount of Olives; and he wept as he went, for God had hurt him exceedingly by this. If some other enemy, stronger and more cunning than Absalom, had risen against him he would have inflicted a great defeat upon him. But now his heart would not permit him to wage war against his son. For what would be the use of his victory if his son were to be among those who fell? But he could not understand why God had punished him so heavily. Yet since it had happened, he wished to accept the judgment in the eyes of all the people.

And so, when they came to the summit of the mountain, he told his men, "Seek me an idol and bring it here to me."

The men went to carry out the king's orders. As they were going, Hushai of Erech, David's friend and counsellor, met them, and he asked:

"Where are you going?"

"The king has sent us to find him an idol," said they.

Hushai of Erech was shocked to hear this, and he hastened to the king and said to him: "Is this true? I have heard from your servants that you desire an idol."

"It is perfectly true and correct," answered David. "As soon as the idol is brought, I shall prostrate myself before it to the ground."

When Hushai of Erech heard these dreadful words he quivered and trembled, and he tore his robe and put dust on his head, mourning as though for the dead. In his grief and pain he turned to David and cried:

"How can you dare to prostrate yourself to an idol of wood or stone when the Lord your God has anointed you king over your people? Do you not know that all the people have their eyes on you? They model all their deeds after you."

"I know it well," answered David. "I have a great name all over the country, and the people know that I am righteous and God-fearing, and that I try to treat men well and to do kindness for my people. Yet what will they say now, when they hear that in return for all these deeds my son has risen against me and wishes to kill me? Will they not begin to think wrongly of the Lord and His ways? Will they not say that trouble and distress have come to a man as righteous and noble and full of good deeds as David, and that is a sign that there is neither justice nor judge in Heaven? And so I have made up my mind to bow down before an idol. When people hear how severely I am punished—that my son has risen up to slay me—they will know that it is a fitting recompense from the Lord."

Hushai of Erech, David's good counsellor, did not now what answer to give him. But he sent a message after David's men and explained why the king had asked for the idol. So they decided to return to David empty-handed.

But David understood that his counsellor had intervened. So he laughed and said, "I forgot to tell you that I wanted the idol only in order to smash it afterwards."

11

DAVID KING OF ISRAEL
LIVES FOREVER

WHEN KING DAVID grew very old, he felt that the time was coming for him to die. So he prayed to the Lord, thanked Him for all the wonders which He had done for Israel His people at his hands, and entreated Him for forgiveness and atonement for all the sins he had committed in his life. Then he cried:

"Master of the Universe, inform me, O Lord, what my end is going to be, so that I may know how unimportant I am."

While he was still standing and waiting for the answer of the Lord there suddenly came a great and mighty wind, violent enough to move hills and break rocks. But David knew that the Lord is not in the wind, and he went on waiting.

Out of the wind suddenly came a great noise like the beating of mighty breakers in the sea, waves strong enough to destroy everything

in their path. Yet David knew that the Lord is
not in noise and clatter. And he went on waiting,
quietly and calmly.

The noise died down; then a great fire suddenly burst out all around, like the holy fire of
the altar descending on the daily sacrifice. Yet
David knew that the Lord is not in the fire, and
so he waited still longer for God's answer.

All of a sudden the fire died down and vanished as though it had never been. And the
sound of a fine silence, like the stillness of the
stars at night, like the silence of leaves on summer evenings, of ears of wheat in the field at
noontime, now made itself felt, faint and very
very delicate, sounding to the hearkening ear
like a fine faraway melody with the most delicate
of notes and tones; nothing could compare with
its whispering cadences of beauty. Then David
knew that the Glory of the Lord had filled his
house; he prostrated himself to the ground and
repeated his question:

"O Lord, tell me of my end and the measure
of my days, so that I may know how little I am
worth."

Out of the fine silence the voice of the Lord
answered him:

"It has been decreed by Me, David My son, that the measure of a man's days is not told in advance."

"I know, O Lord," whispered David's lips, "of Thy decree, and I have regarded it as very just. For the moment a man knows the day of his death, no matter how distant it may be, he will regard himself as dead. And I have also heard from Thy holy prophets that of the thousand years which Thou hast granted for the life of Adam, father of all men, Thou gavest him but nine hundred and thirty. The other seventy Thou didst set aside for me, for otherwise I would have perished yet before I was born. But now I am seventy years old, and I know full well that the span of my life is drawing to its close. Therefore I entreat Thee to grant me only this—that Thou reveal to me which day of the week is going to be my last."

The Lord saw that His decree no longer applied to David; out of the silence came his voice, like a silken, caressing whisper:

"You will pass away on the Sabbath."

But David did not wish to pass away on a day on which he sang his songs. So he began to entreat the Lord:

"I pray Thee, O Lord, do not take my soul from me on a Sabbath, but let me perish on the day after."

"I have already set that day aside for making your son Solomon king; and far be it from me to shorten the time of his reign by a single day in order to have you reigning in his place."

"In that case," David went on beseeching, "let my death come a day earlier, so that I may die on the eve of Sabbath."

"Far be it from me to do such a thing," answered the voice of the Lord out of the silence. "For neither shall I diminish the time of *your* reign by a single moment; all the more as I prefer one day which you spend studying the Torah and engaging in song, to thousands of offerings which your son will make to me on the altar."

Then the silence ceased to echo with its fine and fragrant notes, and it became an ordinary quiet, like the stillness that was always to be found in David's house when he sat alone. And so the king knew that the Glory of God had departed; and his death was decreed for one of the coming Sabbaths.

After that day David used to engage in the study of the Torah and in song whenever the

Sabbath day came around. All day long he continued praising the works and the ways of the Lord, for indeed David was a great singer whose like has not been in the world from then until now.

Now when the Sabbath day came which the Lord had appointed to be the last in David's life, the angel of death came to take his soul. But the angel found him singing the praises of the Lord and saying:

"The heavens are the heavens of the Lord
But the earth He hath given unto Mankind.
The dead are not they who praise the Lord
Nor all who go down to the silence.
But we shall praise the Lord
Now and evermore, Halleluyah![1]

When the angel of death heard this lofty song he dared not take David's soul. So he stood waiting for David to finish. But David did not finish. Instead, his song became ever louder, stronger and loftier.

The angel saw that he was waiting in vain. He knew very well that David meant to go on and on, without stopping. And so he felt worried

---

1. Psalms 115:16-18.

that he might be late in carrying out his mission. The day would pass and he would not take the soul of David. He tried once to place his death-dealing hand on his victim; but he could not. The spirit of song guarded David and served like a fortified wall against death.

Not knowing what to do, the angel of death paced to and fro round David's palace, the magnificent house of cedars; in anger he began to shake the trees and make them sway. A great noise started in the garden, that seemed like a storm. When David heard this noise he was greatly astonished, for it was neither autumn nor winter but a hot early summer day, at the loveliest season of the year. So he went swiftly to see what was happening. Yet even on the way there he went on singing. For his entire soul was filled with this song, so that he could not contain it within him.

But as he went in haste, carried on the waves of his singing, one of the steps on the stairway suddenly broke underfoot. He tottered, and his song ceased for a moment. In that brief moment the angel of death, who had been following him like a shadow, swooped down upon him and seized him. David fell lifeless to the

ground, while the angel of death returned to the place from which he came, bearing his capture under his black wings.

Yet the angel who bore death did not know that he had taken away only the spirit of life from David. He was unable to touch David's great song, and it still sounds in the world to this day. It goes on forever, and will never cease.

David King of Israel is not dead, but lives forever. What you have heard from those who should know is perfectly true. David King of Israel lives forever.

12

DAVID'S HARP

Nowhere in the whole world has there been a man who could play the harp to compare with David King of Israel. While he was still a young lad he had been summoned to play the harp before King Saul and drive away the evil spirit that distressed the mournful king. For indeed, Saul suffered greatly on account of this evil spirit, which visited him from time to time. At such moments the king was exceedingly unhappy, and black dread would descend upon him. He would fear his very shadow, for he thought that everybody desired to kill him. Wherever he turned his eyes he saw terrifying black shapes from which he found no refuge. Yet when he heard the playing of David, these terrifying visions grew bright again; the heavens returned to their wonderful blue, and the sun shone again in its radiance, making men's hearts rejoice. The vast abyss surrounding him in his sick imagination was transformed by the notes of David's harp into a magnificent vision. Once again the summits of the distant mountains were tipped with violet, the cornfields were yellow, and the king's heart rejoiced. For the evil spirit had departed as though it had never troubled him at all.

Years later, when the kingdom was firmly held by David, the Lord allowed him to rest from all his enemies, for he was done with all his wars. Then he would sit in his magnificent cedar house in Jerusalem, his capital city, and give countless thanks to the Lord with songs of praise and the wonderful melodies of his harp.

Sometimes his heart would burst into bitter yet very soft weeping, like the sobbing of a faithful and devoted son who has caused his father grief and now entreats him for forgiveness and atonement. Then gentle, tender notes would mount woefully from his strings; and the Lord knew that David was weeping because God had not found him fit and worthy to build Him a great and magnificent Temple which His holy spirit could inhabit.

Sometimes the harp would burst into joyous and boundlessly happy melodies; then a riot of notes resounded like the clamor of victory on the battlefield, like the shouting of victorious conquerors who returned from defeating the foe, bearing ample spoils with them. And then the Lord knew that David was thanking him for all the great deeds and victories which He had performed through David for the sake of Israel.

And sometimes a quiet, regular melody would rise with fine and delicate notes that poured from the strings, sounding like the whisper of the ears of grain in the cornfields; or it was like the sound of the harvester bearing home his sheaves, like the gurgling of water in the brooks and the rustling of trees in the forest. Then the Lord knew that David was relating by means of his harp how great and wonderful were the deeds of the Lord, who had created the world with so much wisdom, and shared that wisdom of His with mankind.

Every night David's harp hung above his bed. At the midnight hour the north wind blew through the open window and paused amid the strings. The strings would vibrate of themselves, and gentle, delicate melodies, such as no man has ever heard, would rise from the harp.

At the sound of this heavenly melody David

would awaken from his sleep and go up to the roof of his mansion. There he would look down at the grandeur of nature and beauty in Jerusalem his city, with the mountains round about it and the spirit of God always resting upon it. His heart would fill with overflowing melody. He would take his harp and begin playing, playing and singing his fervent songs, the holy songs you find in the Book of Psalms.

When David strummed, the air would be filled with the scent of fragrant perfumes and spices. Flowers of the field would give ear and lower their dew-filled heads, swaying and gleaming in the rhythm of the melody. Birds would hear and wake up in their nests, and they also would begin twittering their own songs. The moon and the stars would hear and begin to leap and dance and quiver on high. Even the silent mountains of Jerusalem seemed to be listening astonished to the sound of the harp; for the cypress trees upon them stirred and swayed their tops as though engaged in silent prayer.

All creation, all the living things and plants therein, were filled with his sacred song. All creation became one single melody exalting and praising the name of the Lord on high. David's harp would begin and Jerusalem would respond, and then all the world would follow and join it.

When the mists of night began to disperse and the eastern horizon grew bright, the morning star rose proclaiming a new day. But David's harp did not cease its melody. For what could he do except play and sing at the sight of the glory that was shed over Jerusalem and her surroundings, when he saw Man going forth to his labors and his works? Beyond, far away, the summits of the mountains of Moab were growing red within the boundaries of his land. Gleaming Jordan and the Dead Sea were like a silver necklace with a great diamond at its end. How could he not sing their praises? And yonder was Bethlehem, the city of his birth, with Rachel's tomb on the highway that leads to Ephrat; while far, far in the distance all round stretched the lofty mountains of Judah, with their gardens and vineyards, their spacious cornfields blessed with grain running down the slopes; there his people worked with their implements to bring forth food from their soil. What else could he do except sing in their honor?

Long after he put down his harp the whole world still rang with his melodies. And therefore

the sound of David's harp did not cease even after David passed away. For the harp still hangs over the bed of the sleeping king in a hidden cave. There is a bowl of water at his head; he has his sword at his side, while his harp remains above him.

Night by night the harp hums and the wind turns the pages of the Book of Psalms lying by the king. Until this day you can hear the sound of his wonderful singing over the summits of the hills which are round about Jerusalem, and at the top of the Tower of David as well.

Happy is the man who is privileged to hear his song. He is listening to the song that heralds the coming of Messiah.

13

THE SWORD OF KING DAVID

KING DAVID has not died. He sleeps in a hidden cave, and no man knows where it is. There he lies resting on a golden bed set with sapphires and diamonds, under a blue canopy that has silver braid hanging from its ends. There he rests, at his feet a candle that burns with a perpetual flame, at his head the trusty sword; and with it lies the shield with the six points from which all shields of David bear their name to this day. On the wall hangs his harp, and with the faint breath of wind that quivers the strings at the midnight hour, it hums and throbs with a sound like distant weeping. On the golden table beside his head rests the Book of Psalms and a bowl of water. Whenever the harp throbs the Book of Psalms opens by itself, and the melody of the harp is accompanied by a soft, soft sighing song.

The king sleeps, sleeps ... and waits for

somebody to come and awaken him. Then the king will stretch out his hands. And if the man who has aroused him pours water swiftly on his hands from the golden bowl, the king will give that man his sword. With it he can gather the dispersed sons of Israel from the nations and bring them to Jerusalem, which is the city of David forever.

But years have passed, many many years; and no man comes to awaken him.

It is true that many courageous, choice young men have heard the tale of the sleeping king in his hidden cave, and have been captivated by this great vision of redemption. Their hearts have yearned to receive the redeeming sword at the hands of King David. In every generation there have been those who have risen up and girded their loins, and have forsaken their homes to seek for the cave of King David. Yet they grew weary on the way to a place they could not know, and returned as they started out, sad and unhappy. Others, more daring and courageous, staunchly said, "We shall continue on our way, no matter what happens to us." These met with many great difficulties and obstacles, and fell to rise no more. The handful whose vision and faith enabled them to overcome every obstacle and continue on their way—these were the prey of wild beasts, vipers, adders and terrifying monsters; and they too never reached the place of their desire. Yet in spite of this there have always been other youths who are carried away by the vision and follow in their footsteps.

On one occasion, so runs the tale, two brave lads succeeded in reaching the cave and entered it. Yet when they saw the gold and precious stones covering the cave's walls, when they saw the glorious blue canopy and heard the melody of the wondrous harp, their eyes were dazzled by the light, and in their great confusion they did not even notice King David raising his hands to them. And so they forgot to pour water on his hands from the bowl. The king sighed and drew his hands back, and when the two brave lads awakened from their astonishment, they found themselves deep in a vast desert without any track or path. Then they knew they had missed the favorable hour, and their hearts burst with anguish and grief. Both found their deaths in that terrible desert.

But brave and daring lads remain, prepared to seek for the cave of King David like their comrades of whom no trace remains. For they yearn and long to redeem their people, who were and are being persecuted by the heathen.

Now two such lads studied together under a great teacher. And one day they agreed to start out together and obtain the redeeming sword from King David. They did not go empty-handed. They girded short daggers at their waists, and the fire of love burned in their eyes; their hearts were filled with the spirit of God, and they were both prepared to overcome any obstacle, to outface any monstrous beast and fight it for life or death. They resolved to reach the cave come what might; then they would rouse the slumbering king from his sleep and bring redemption speedily to their people; for their people could bear their suffering no more. The cruel heathen were drowning their brethren in their own tears and blood.

Many who heard of this wished to persuade the two boys to give up their idea. Some shook their heads over them as you shake your head over the dead, grieving for the young lives that would be lost. Others said that the two lads would bring calamity upon themselves, and not only upon themselves but upon all their people.

For how could they prove stronger than the many powerful nations and peoples? And there were ever so many others who mocked at them. They called them hotheads, and said they were crazed. It was hard for the two young men to bear the pity of their friends. It was sevenfold harder to bear the words of those with little faith, whos servitude made them fear the light of freedom. Yet seven and seventy times more difficult did they find it to bear the mockery, which pierced their hearts like a sword. But in spite of this they set out on their perilous but promising way, hoping that a great light might yet shine on their people because of them.

So the two brave lads set out to seek the cave of King David. They went on and on for days and weeks and months. When one grew weary the other would encourage him, and carry him if necessary. If one grew thirsty the other would gather dewdrops and bring them to his companion's mouth. They never lost heart, because of their great love.

They went on and on by day and night; they went on and on for days and weeks and months and years. When they came to a rock face that was upright as a wall, they hacked at it with

116

their hands until they cleft themselves a tunnel through which to pass. If they came to a valley that was as deep as an abyss they piled up stones and earth till it served them as a bridge.

They went on and on by day and night; they went on and on for days and years. If a wild beast lay in ambush waiting for them, they leapt at it with their daggers; if it pounced upon them, they met it face to face; and always they drove it away wounded and howling. Sometimes they even cut it to pieces with their keen-bladed daggers. They were torn and scratched and wounded, starving and lonely on the way, but they went on. Their daggers were tied round their waists, the spirit of God was in the heart, and in their mouths was a song of the redemption which was going to come about—thanks to them.

And thanks to their faith and belief that the Lord would help them succeed, thanks to the keen-bladed daggers and the arms that they raised fearlessly against all that rose to stop them, signs of redemption began to appear. Strange things, visions which no man could imagine, came to happen before their eyes.

One day, as they rested under a date palm which grew solitary in the wilderness, they saw

117

a dove that was seated among the leaves, moaning to herself and weeping.

Remembering how they had once learned that Israel is likened to a dove, they turned to her and asked:

"Innocent turtledove, precious and dear,
Is the grave of King David far off or near?"

The dove flapped her wings and said in human speech:

"The eagle, the eagle my young did slay,
Burned up my nest and it drove me away—
But go you and ask of the flowing river."

That was what the dove said, and then she became silent and would utter not one word more.

Then the two brave lads knew that this dove was the Daughter of Zion, and it wept because Rome, the great and preying eagle, had burned the Temple and driven her from her land and took away all her children. The fact that she had come to them was in itself a sign of redemption.

Though shaken, they were yet heartened. On they went until they came to a great river. They wished to quench their thirst in its waters, but then they saw that this was not water flowing

but blood. And from the blood cried the voice of countless slaughtered Jewish children:

"The eagle, the eagle after the slaughter
Washed off its claws within my clear water—
To the mountain with you, for the straight
way is there."

Then the two lands knew they must approach the mountain which they could see in the distance.

Breathlessly they hastened there. As they reached the slopes they paused; and all at once they saw an old man with a white beard that came down to his waist and a leather girdle about him, his eyes glowing with a pure and holy light. The man was coming toward them. This, they knew at once, must be the Tishbite Elijah who will herald the Redeemer. For as they had pictured him in their dreams, so they now saw him standing before them, in all his splendor and radiance.

The two brave lads greeted him with peace. He responded with a blessing of peace, and rejoiced to see them. He kissed them on their brows, and they felt as though a father were kissing the children who had returned to him after a long, long journey from far away.

Then the old man approached a great stone that lay on the lower slope of the mountain, and he gave a gentle order: "Stone, stone, roll away."

His words sounded like a whispered prayer. The old man repeated them a second and a third time. Suddenly the stone rolled away and a sweet fragrance rose to them from the mouth of the cave.

"Go forward!" said the Tishbite to the lads. "The king sleeps his sleep in this cave, and his sword is waiting for you. Take it and do wonders, and bring salvation with it. Advance from victory to victory, and may foe after foe fall before you. Do not rest or pause until you will have taken the entire land, all that the Lord has promised to your forefathers. For if you stand still on the road of your salvation, the sword will vanish and return to this hidden cave."

So he spoke. Then he vanished in a blaze of fire that mounted aloft.

With hearts that beat like hammer blows, yet with assured paces, the two brave lads went down into the cave. In the cave the walls shone with gold, and thousands of sapphires, rubies and diamonds dazzled their eyes. The gentle

sound of a harp enchanted their ears, and the fragrances of Eden made their heads swim.

Yet the two brave lads did not delay for even a single moment, or turn their eyes to all these. What did they care for all this gold and the precious jewels? What were all these worth compared with the gleaming sword of King David? They paid no attention to the murmuring of the wonderful harp; for they knew they would hear melodies more wonderful than these when they proclaimed freedom over the mountains of Jerusalem. Even the fragrance of the fine scents did not make them languish or put them to sleep, for their souls were always longing for some other sweet savor—the sweet savor that would rise in the future from the Mountain of Myrrh and would spread across all the mountains of the Land of Israel.

No, they were not led astray by all these, for the redeeming sword was more precious to them than anything else. As they approached the golden bed they saw that the king was holding his hands out to them; swiftly they poured forth the water from the waiting bowl.

The earth shook beneath them, and overhead the mountain trembled. A great light, as the light of the seven days of creation, broke forth before their eyes, and they fell on their faces. But when they rose they found themselves standing at the gates of Jerusalem, holding the sword of David king of Israel.

In all its splendor, they brandished it aloft.

Then from every side they saw the young men of Israel coming, gathering and marching against the foes who swooped down upon them on every side. The brave soldiers of Israel vanquished their enemy once and for all.

There was then a great salvation and a mighty victory indeed. But when the two youths saw the enemy fleeing from them in confusion they forgot the words of the Tishbite in their great joy; they paused in the fighting in order to rest a moment. When they prepared to begin afresh, they no longer found the sword, for it had vanished and gone.